Elsa puts on gloves to block her powers. She decides not to play
with her sister any more.

The sisters grow apart as they get older.

Prince Hans has sailed to Arendelle from afar for the celebrations.

Princess Anna knocks into Hans's horse and falls into a boat,
but Hans is pleased to meet her.

The sisters are ready for the big day – Elsa is going to be crowned
Queen of Arendelle.

Elsa holds the sceptre and orb in her bare hands
without freezing them, while Anna stands by her side.

Queen Elsa doesn't approve of Anna's quick engagement to Hans.
As they argue Anna pulls off Elsa's gloves.

Elsa cannot control her powers because she is upset and
she accidentally blasts ice everywhere.

The people of Arendelle are frightened of Elsa's powers.
Even Anna is shocked to finally learn Elsa's secret.

Queen Elsa runs away from Arendelle.
As she leaves, snow and ice cover the ground.

Anna decides to go after Elsa. She asks Hans
to take care of the kingdom while she is away.

Once she is alone Elsa is finally free to use her powers.
She builds a stunning ice palace.

Elsa becomes the Snow Queen and practises her icy powers.

Princess Anna rides her horse through the winter storm in the mountains.

Anna is thrown from her horse and lands in the snow.
Luckily she finds shelter in a remote shop.

Anna meets a snow-covered Kristoff inside the small shop.
He's not happy about the winter storm!

Oaken is the owner of the shop, which sells supplies to travellers.

Kristoff is an expert mountain man.

He is thrown out of the shop after he calls Oaken a 'crook'.

Kristoff's best friend is a reindeer called Sven.

Anna asks for Kristoff's help to find her sister.
To persuade him she gives some carrots to Sven.

The three new friends get into trouble when a pack of wolves chase their sledge off the side of a mountain.

Kristoff loses his sledge and most of his belongings.
Anna promises to replace everything.

Anna, Kristoff and Sven find Elsa's icy wonderland –
and a walking, talking snowman called Olaf!

Olaf is a magical snowman who likes warm hugs.

Anna realizes that Olaf looks like the snowman that Elsa made for her as a child. She realizes that her new friend has been created by her sister.

Olaf may be made of snow, but he'd love to
spend some time relaxing in the summer sun.

Sven and Olaf quickly become friends,
even though Sven tries to eat Olaf's carrot nose!

When Anna's horse returns to Arendelle without her Prince Hans sets off to find her.

Olaf shows Anna, Kristoff and Sven the way to the ice palace.

The ice palace looks magnificent at the top of the North Mountain.

Anna, Kristoff, Sven and Olaf meet Elsa the Snow Queen.

Anna asks Elsa to return to Arendelle but Elsa refuses.

The sisters argue about their differences.

Although she doesn't mean to, Elsa hits Anna in the chest with a blast of ice because she can't control her powers when she is upset.

Elsa creates a giant snowman called Marshmallow!

Marshmallow runs after Anna and Kristoff.

As they try to escape from Marshmallow
Kristoff helps Anna down the side of a cliff.

Suddenly Anna's hair starts to turn white.
Elsa's blast of ice has put a powerful curse on her.

Elsa is upset about striking her sister with ice
and not being able to control her magic.

Kristo

The olde

but that an a

Kristoff rushes Anna back to Aren

A true love's kiss from H

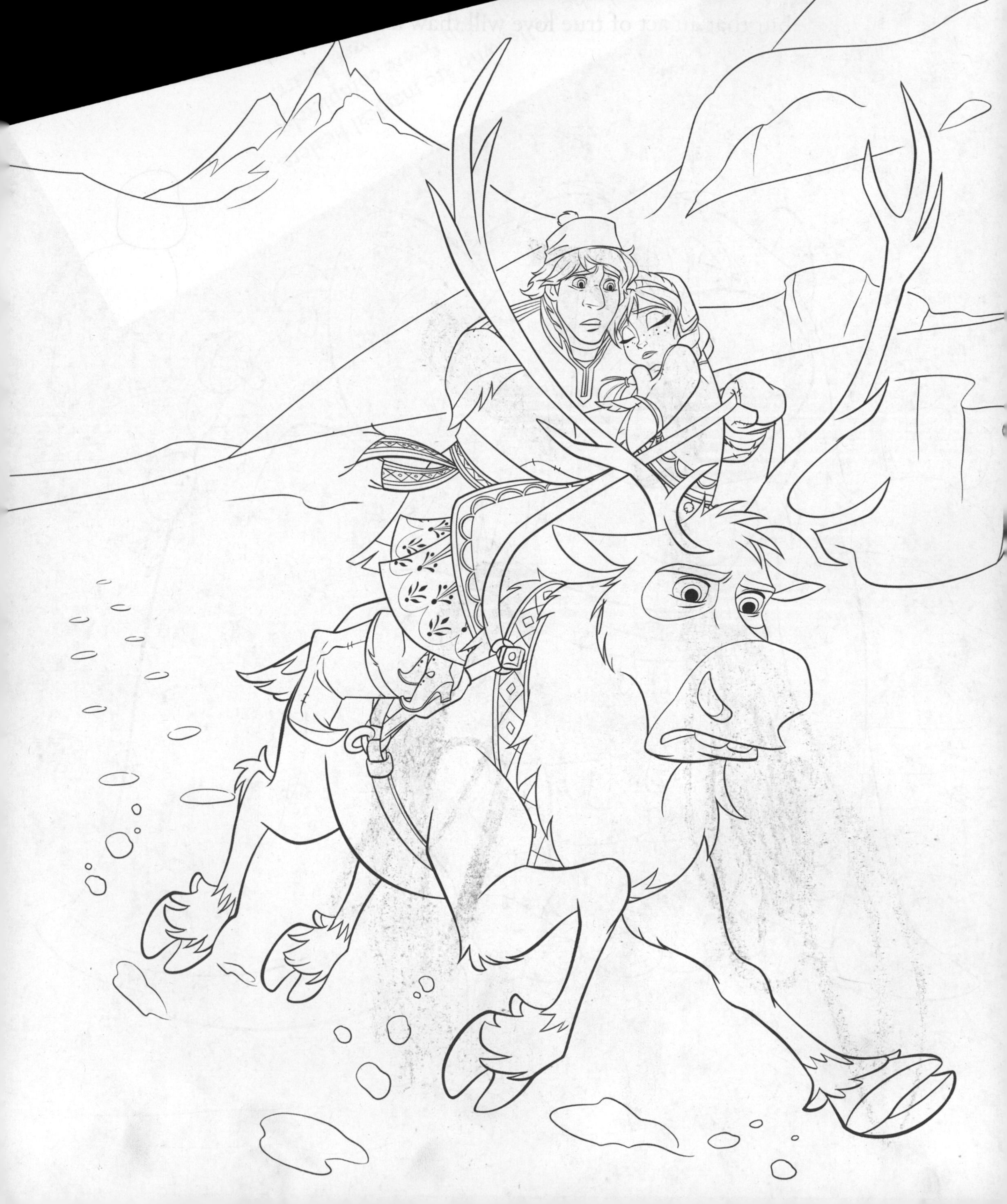

arrives at the ice palace, Elsa defends
men in his group try to capture her.

Kristoff rushes Anna back to Arendelle.
A true love's kiss from Hans should save her.

Kristoff takes Anna to the trolls, who are magical healers.
The oldest troll says Anna will soon freeze completely,
but that an act of true love will thaw a frozen heart.

Prince Hans goes to Anna, but refuses to kiss her!
He says he never loved her and locks her away as she slowly freezes.

Sven wants Kristoff to return to Arendelle because he knows that Kristoff loves Anna.

Anna manages to escape from the castle but she is freezing to her core –
can an act of true love save her?

Anna is almost frozen when Kristoff returns to Arendelle.
His kiss might save her ...

... but Anna sees that her sister is in danger as Hans sneaks up behind
Anna needs to help her sister, but without Kristoff's kiss she will die.

Anna saves her sister by jumping in front of Elsa as Hans tries
to strike her with his sword. Anna turns to ice and the sword snaps.

Kristoff makes sure that Hans cannot strike a second blow.

Elsa hugs her sister and cries as she realizes that Anna has saved her life.

But Anna's act of true love for her sister means that
the spell is broken. Anna is no longer frozen!

Olaf starts to melt as the kingdom starts to thaw,
but Elsa helps him with her powers.

Kristoff, Anna, Elsa and even Olaf are happy that summer has returned to Arendelle.

Anna keeps her promise and gives Kristoff a new sledge.
He decides to stay in Arendelle – with Anna!